Based on an original idea by Alex A.

First published in French in 2013 by Presses Aventure under the title
La prophétie des quatre.

Published by **Adventure Press**, an imprint of:
Les Publications Modus Vivendi Inc.
55 Jean-Talon Street West
Montreal, Quebec, Canada H2R 2W8
adventurepress.ca

Publisher: Marc G. Alain
Editorial Director: Marie-Eve Labelle
Author and illustrator: Alex A.
Page layout: Vicky Masse
Translator: Rhonda Mullins

Legal deposit – Bibliothèque et Archives nationales du Québec, 2016
Legal deposit – Library and Archives Canada, 2016

ISBN 978-1-77285-000-0 (PAPERBACK)

ISBN 978-1-77285-001-7 (PDF)
ISBN 978-1-77285-002-4 (EPUB)
ISBN 978-1-77285-003-1 (KINDLE)

We gratefully acknowledge the financial support of the Government
of Canada through the Canada Book Fund (CBF) for our publishing activities.

Government of Québec – Tax credit for book publishing – Administered by SODEC

Printed in China

THE PROPHECY OF FOUR

WRITTEN AND ILLUSTRATED
BY ALEX A.

ADVENTURE PRESS

FOR AMÉLY,
AMBASSADOR OF THE NUMBER 4.

PRESENT DAY...

WELCOME TO MY DOJO, JON LE BON.

MY NAME IS **NOAH**. FOR THE NEXT YEAR I WILL BE YOUR MARTIAL ARTS TEACHER AND YOUR SPIRITUAL GUIDE.

YOU WILL LEARN THE TECHNIQUES OF A STYLE OF COMBAT THAT HAS SURVIVED MILLENNIA AT THE AGENCY...

THE MAD DRAGON.

COOL!

BUT THE PATH WILL NOT BE AN EASY ONE. YOU WILL HAVE TO THINK LIKE A MONK AND BEND LIKE BAMBOO.

UM... OK! BUT I CAN'T MAKE ANY PROMISES.

NOW... SHOW ME WHAT YOU'RE MADE OF.

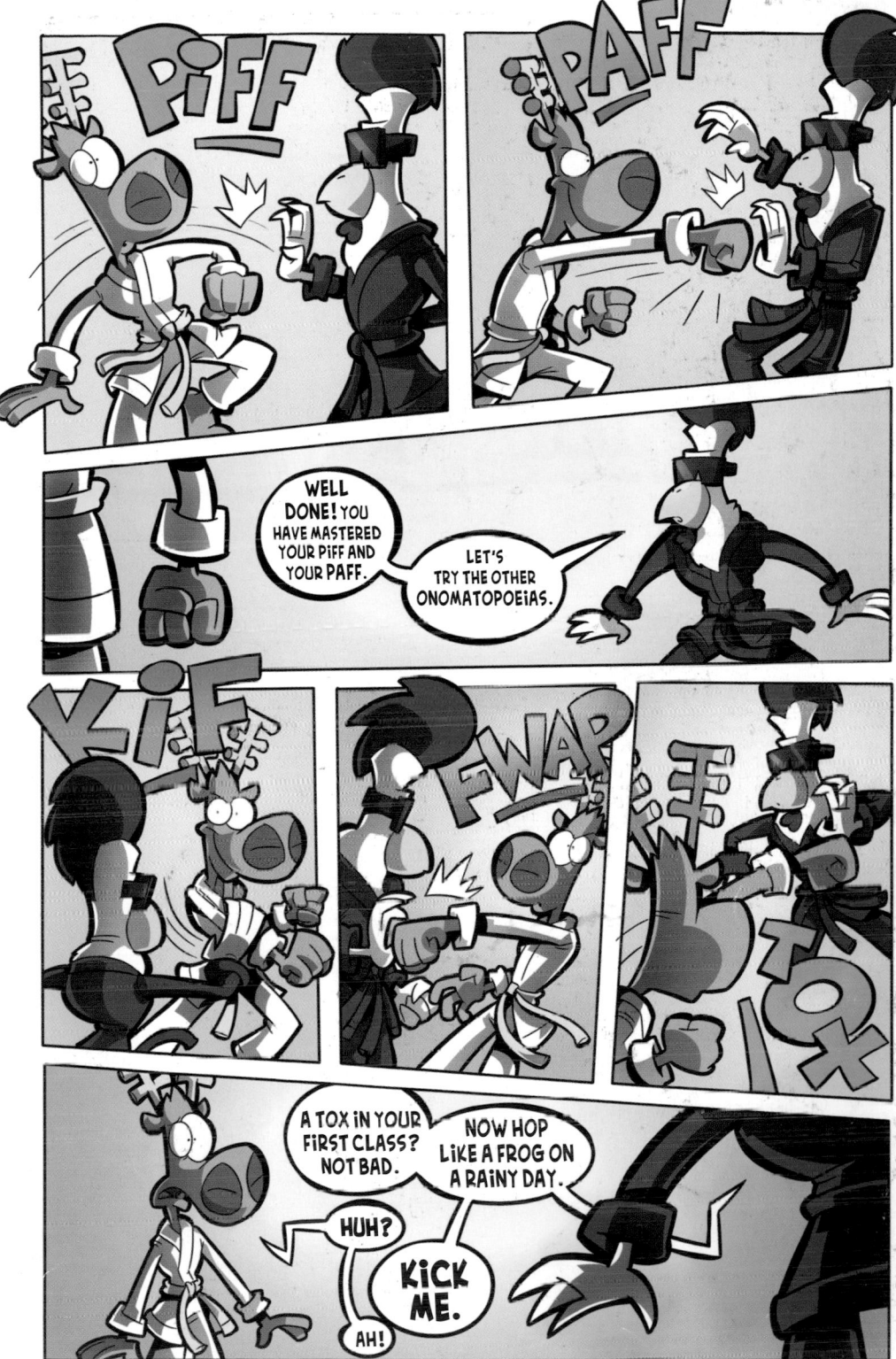

HENRY, WHERE ARE WE AT WITH THE RESEARCH INTO PURPLE MATTER? HAVE YOU FOUND A WAY TO REGULATE THE SYSTEM?

HENRY?

UM... YES, YES MA'AM! I'LL BRING YOU THE RESULTS IN A FEW MINUTES. BUT THERE'S SOMETHING I NEED TO FINISH UP HERE FIRST...

EXCELLENT. I'LL SEE YOU SHORTLY.

SO... IF I ADD THE ANGLE OF INCLINE OF THE CENTRE OF THE GALAXY TO THE HYPOTHETICAL AGE OF THE UNIVERSE...

I DON'T BELIEVE IT...

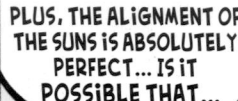

PLUS, THE ALIGNMENT OF THE SUNS IS ABSOLUTELY PERFECT... IS IT POSSIBLE THAT...

NO WAY!

BRRRRRRRRr

AGAIN?

WHAT ARE YOU SAYING, HENRY?

LOOK, I'VE RUN THE NUMBERS. THIS YEAR, THE EARTH WILL BE 4 BILLION YEARS OLD. OUR SUN WILL ENTER ITS 4TH CYCLE AND ALIGN WITH 4 OTHER SUNS AROUND THE MIDDLE OF THE GALAXY, WHICH IS INCLINED 4.444 DEGREES.

AND TODAY, WE HAD THE 4TH EARTHQUAKE IN 4 WEEKS. 4, 4, 4, 4. FOURS EVERYWHERE YOU LOOK! I THINK WE'RE ABOUT TO EXPERIENCE...

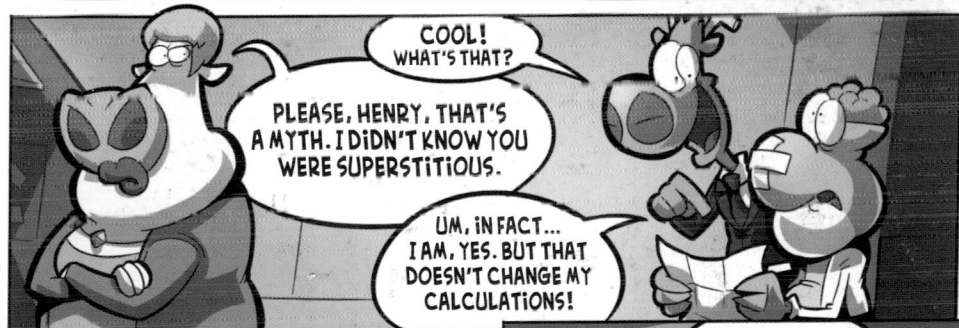

THE PROPHECY OF 4.

COOL! WHAT'S THAT?

PLEASE, HENRY, THAT'S A MYTH. I DIDN'T KNOW YOU WERE SUPERSTITIOUS.

UM, IN FACT... I AM, YES. BUT THAT DOESN'T CHANGE MY CALCULATIONS!

IS THAT TRUE? YOU'RE SUPERSTITIOUS?

YES...

AHH!!

HEE HEE. I'M GOING TO HAVE SOME FUN WITH THIS.

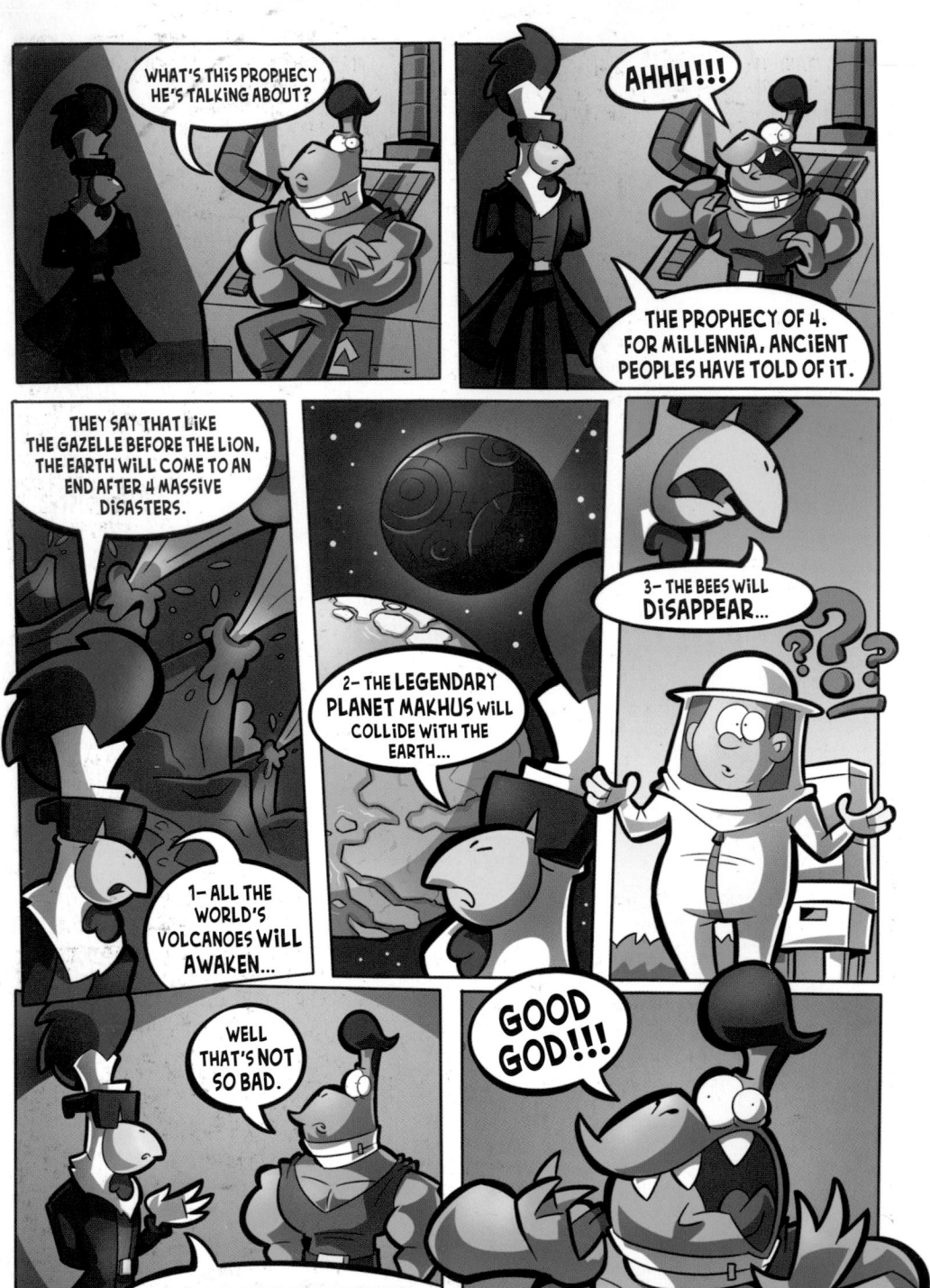

AND 4- WHEN ALL OF THESE EVENTS REACH A PINNACLE, THE GREAT AND POWERFUL DEMON KASTARO WILL RISE AGAIN...

AND DESTROY WHAT REMAINS OF OUR CIVILIZATION, TO REIGN OVER OUR PLANET.

NOW I WILL RETURN TO THE SHADOWS.

EXACTLY! AND THE 4 EARTHQUAKES ARE ONE OF THE WARNING SIGNS! ACCORDING TO MY CALCULATIONS, WE HAVE 4 DAYS BEFORE ALL OF THIS HAPPENS.

HEY, COME TO THINK OF IT... IT'S THE 4TH APOCALYPSE WE'VE HAD TO PREVENT THIS YEAR.

YOU SEE!!!

AHHH! THAT BURNS!!!

HEE HEE! HE REALLY IS SUPERSTITIOUS!

THAT'S ALL WELL AND GOOD, BUT YOU'VE FORGOTTEN ONE THING. NOAH, WHAT ARE THE OTHER WARNING SIGNS?

4 DAYS BEFOREHAND, THE SKY WILL TURN RED LIKE TOMATO PASTE. THAT IS THE PROPHECY.

THANK YOU, NOAH.

AND IS THE SKY RED TODAY?

NEVER HEARD OF IT. WHAT IS IT?

AHH!

THE REDLANDS, OR, AS THE ANCIENT PEOPLES CALLED IT...

THE PLAINS OF BLOOD.

IN ADDITION TO THE EXCRUCIATING HEAT AND HEAVILY POLLUTED AIR, THE REDLANDS ARE POPULATED WITH MYTHICAL CREATURES, MURDEROUS DOWN TO THE LAST ONE.

LIKE MINOTAURS...

GARGOYLES...

AND ALAN THE BANANA.

UM, YES. THANKS AGAIN, NOAH...

21

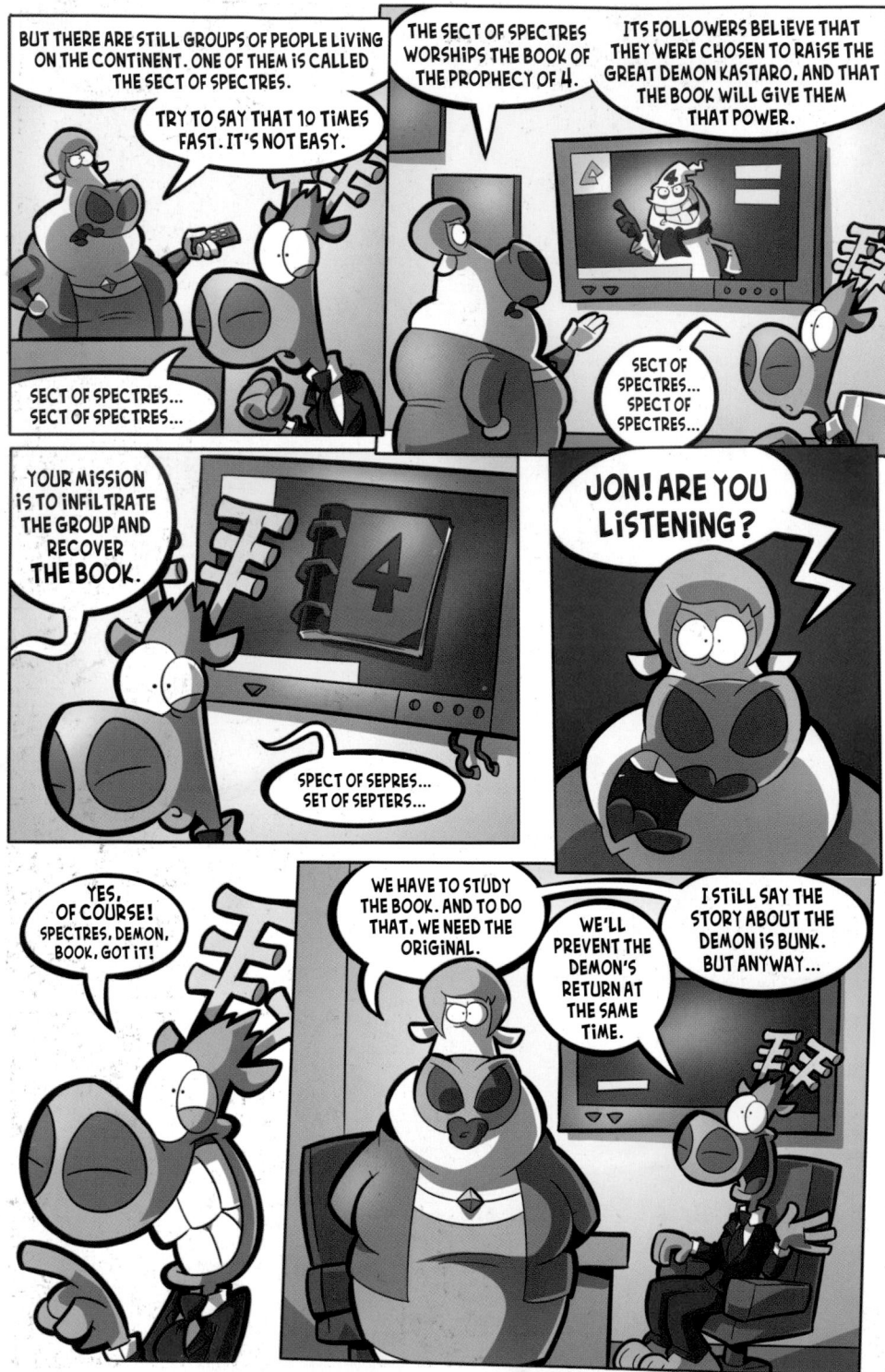

BUT THERE ARE STILL GROUPS OF PEOPLE LIVING ON THE CONTINENT. ONE OF THEM IS CALLED THE SECT OF SPECTRES.

TRY TO SAY THAT 10 TIMES FAST. IT'S NOT EASY.

SECT OF SPECTRES... SECT OF SPECTRES...

THE SECT OF SPECTRES WORSHIPS THE BOOK OF THE PROPHECY OF 4.

ITS FOLLOWERS BELIEVE THAT THEY WERE CHOSEN TO RAISE THE GREAT DEMON KASTARO, AND THAT THE BOOK WILL GIVE THEM THAT POWER.

SECT OF SPECTRES... SPECT OF SPECTRES...

YOUR MISSION IS TO INFILTRATE THE GROUP AND RECOVER THE BOOK.

SPECT OF SEPRES... SET OF SEPTERS...

JON! ARE YOU LISTENING?

YES, OF COURSE! SPECTRES, DEMON, BOOK, GOT IT!

WE HAVE TO STUDY THE BOOK. AND TO DO THAT, WE NEED THE ORIGINAL.

WE'LL PREVENT THE DEMON'S RETURN AT THE SAME TIME.

I STILL SAY THE STORY ABOUT THE DEMON IS BUNK. BUT ANYWAY...

IT WAS LIKE YOU WERE HAVING A DISTURBING VISION. I HAVE CARAMELS IF YOU LIKE!

NO, I'LL BE FINE. HENRY AND SHORTHAND ARE WAITING FOR YOU IN THE BASEMENT. THAT WILL BE ALL.

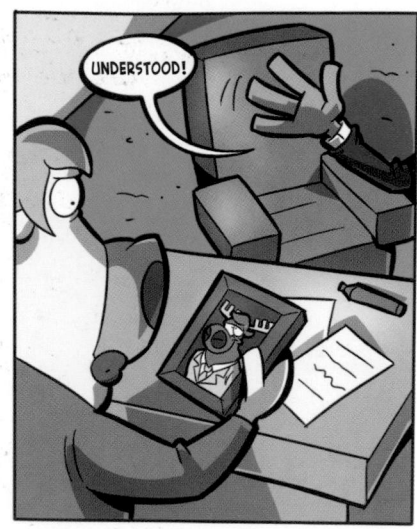

UNDERSTOOD!

JON, THIS MISSION IS BY FAR THE MOST DANGEROUS YOU HAVE TAKEN ON SINCE YOU'VE BEEN ON ACTIVE DUTY.

TRY TO COME BACK ALIVE.

HA! I WILL DEFINITELY COME BACK ALIVE!

HOW WOULD I COME BACK IF I WERE DEAD?

...

CAN YOU GET OUT OF MY OFFICE NOW?!

... NO.

OK, WE HAVE TO COME UP WITH A DISGUISE THAT MAKES HIM LOOK LIKE SOMEONE WHO LIVES IN THE REDLANDS.

THAT SHOULDN'T BE TOO HARD. CAN YOU PLAY A BAD GUY, JON?

UH-HUH... WE'VE GOT OUR WORK CUT OUT FOR US.

I HAVE A HARD TIME GETTING INTO CHARACTER IF I'M NOT IN COSTUME.

WE'LL FIX THAT...

PUT ON THIS COAT. THAT'S A START...

YOU NEED A BIT MORE BLACK UNDER THE EYES...

YOUR NAME IS BORIS ROGANOFF NOW.

LOOK AT THIS, JON. I USED THE AGENCY'S SUPERVILLAIN ARCHIVES TO FIND YOU A CHARACTER.

A BLOODTHIRSTY MERCENARY BORN IN THE REDLANDS OVER 100 YEARS AGO.

HE WAS ONE OF THE AGENCY'S TOP ENEMIES AT ONE TIME.

WE NEED TO DO SOMETHING ABOUT THESE ANTLERS...

LET'S HOPE THEY BUY IT...

DAUCUS CAROTA! DAUCUS CAROTA!

UM... BUT I'VE NEVER HEARD OF YOU, SERIOUSLY...

HUH? WHAT DO YOU MEAN YOU'VE NEVER HEARD OF US? WE'RE NEO-MARTIANS! THE LEGENDARY PEOPLE KNOWN THROUGHOUT THE GALAXIES!

UM, NO, NEVER HEARD OF YOU... SORRY! BUT YOU LOOK GREAT.

YOU'VE NEVER EVEN HEARD ABOUT OUR GOD?

HORUS! HORUS! HORUS!

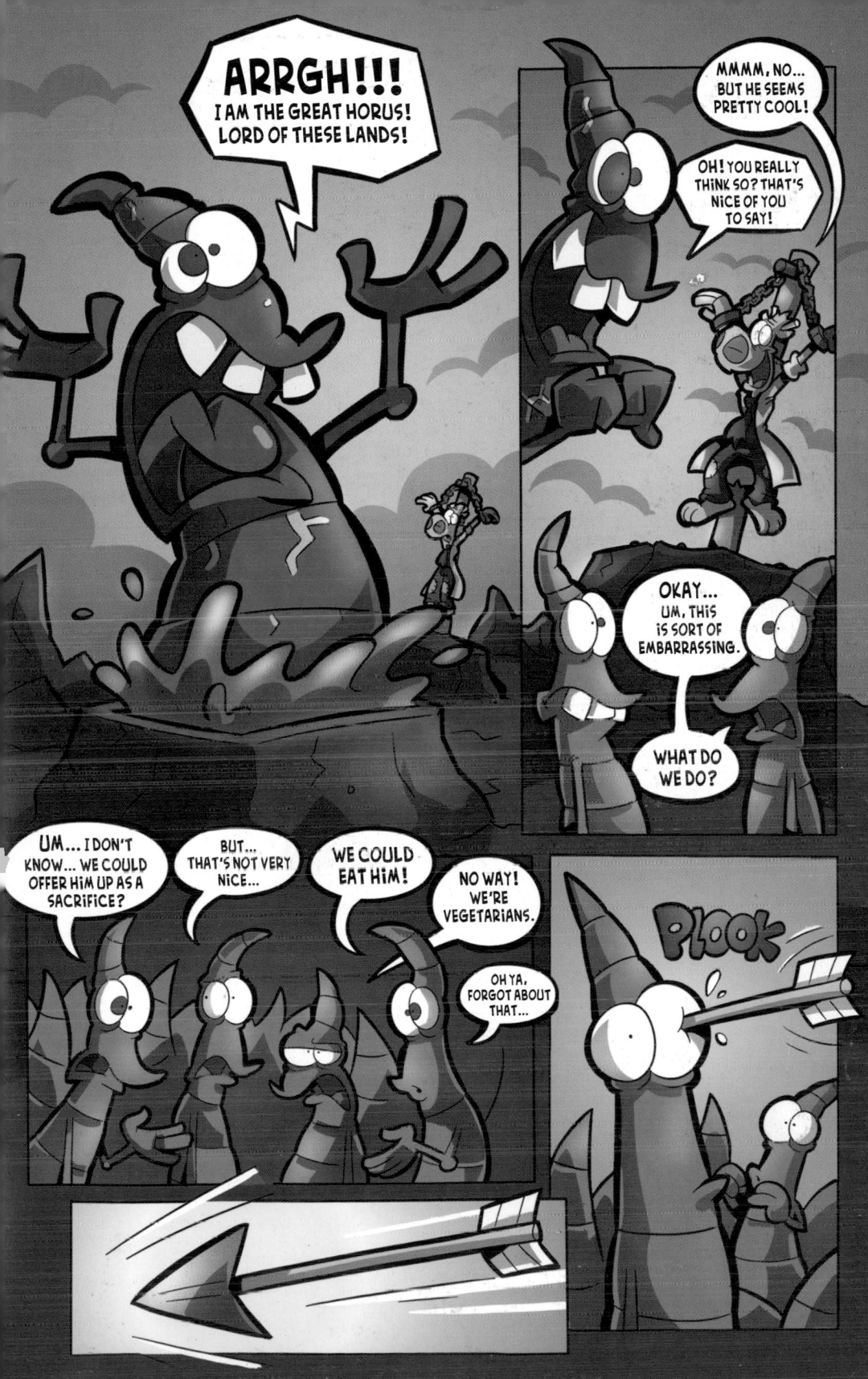

FURY, NOW!

AHHH!
FIRE AND PUNCHES TO THE FACE! THEY FOUND OUR WEAK POINT!

YOU. COME WITH US.

UM... OK!

AND THIS IS FURY, MY SON.

PLEASURE! ARGHEU!!!

IS HE ALRIGHT?

OH, DON'T WORRY ABOUT HIM. HIS OXYGEN SUPPLY WAS CUT OFF A LITTLE WHEN HE WAS BORN.

AND THE TWO OF US ARE PART OF THE...

CLUB OF REBELS.

THE CLUB OF REBELS?

YA, I KNOW. IT'S NOT VERY "COOL"... WE HAD A LOT OF TROUBLE COMING UP WITH A NAME. BUT IN THE END...

ARGHEU!

WE SAVED YOU BECAUSE WE NEED NEW YOUNG, ENERGETIC BLOOD LIKE YOU ON OUR TEAM.

YOU MAY NOT KNOW WHO YOU ARE, BUT, JUDGING FROM YOUR APPEARANCE, I'D SAY YOU'RE A TOUGH GUY... LOOK.

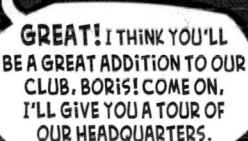

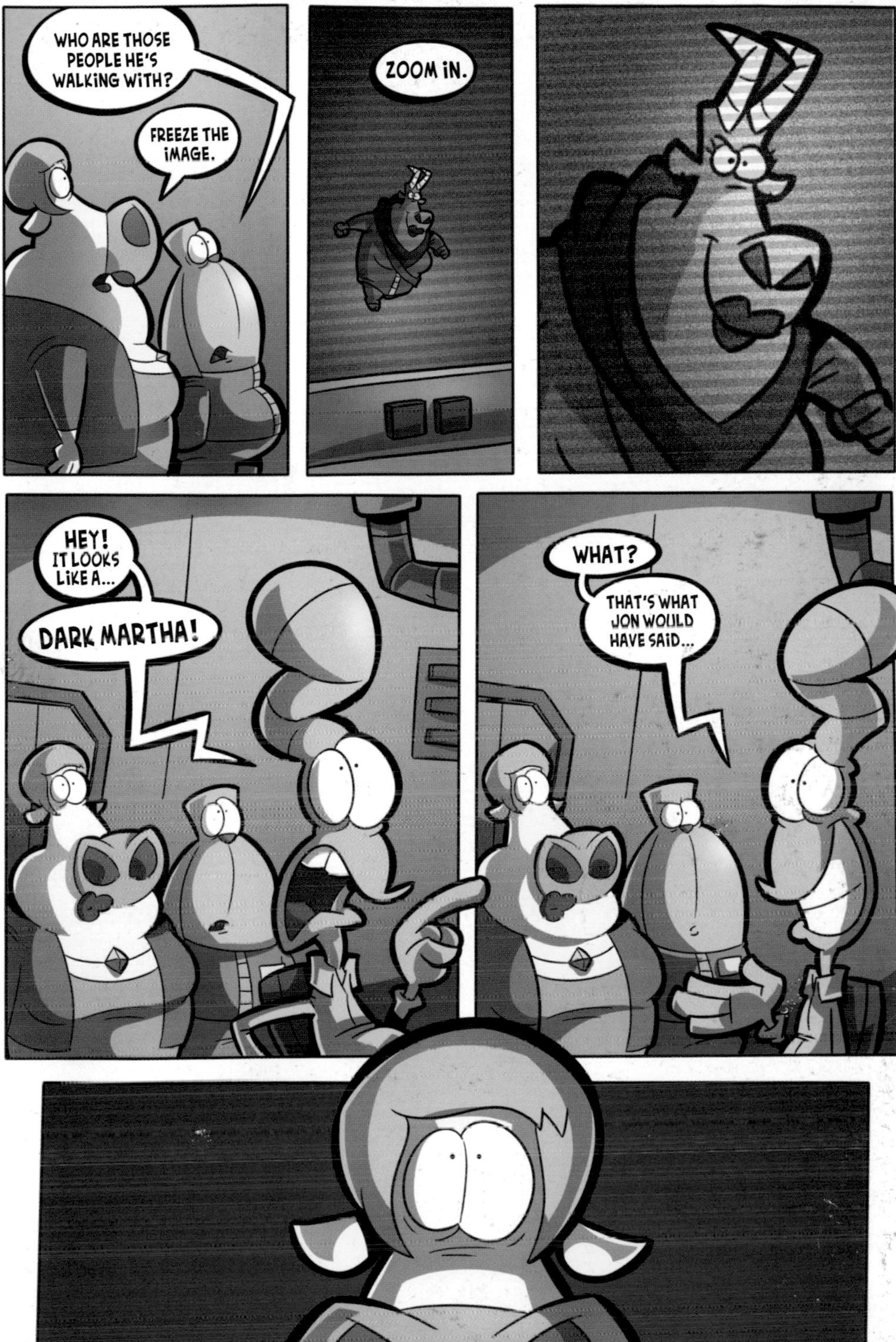

WHO ARE THOSE PEOPLE HE'S WALKING WITH?

FREEZE THE IMAGE.

ZOOM IN.

HEY! IT LOOKS LIKE A...

DARK MARTHA!

WHAT?

THAT'S WHAT JON WOULD HAVE SAID...

AH! YES, UM...

FEELING A LITTLE "HYPOGLYCEMIC" AGAIN?

NO... I... I KNOW THAT PERSON.

HER NAME IS CASSANDRA. BEFORE I JOINED THE AGENCY, SHE, HYLDA AND I WERE PART OF A GROUP OF LAW ENFORCERS...

THE SISTERHOOD.

UM... WHAT'S UP WITH THE NAME?

I KNOW, I KNOW... WE WERE YOUNG.

ARCHIVES 44

SO, JON IS IN GOOD HANDS?

NOT REALLY.

SHORTHAND, GET THE PLANE READY.

I'M GOING TO THE REDLANDS.

WELCOME TO OUR HOME, BORIS.

WOW. TASTEFULLY DECORATED.

LOVE THE CURTAINS.

I'LL INTRODUCE YOU TO THE OTHER CLUB MEMBERS. **ALAN THE BANANA,** THE REDLANDS' LEGENDARY FEARSOME CREATURE.

AND AN EXCELLENT SOURCE OF POTASSIUM.

THAT'S HOSTILIA, OUR SCIENTIST.

YOU LOOK FAMILIAR...

I HAVE ONE OF THOSE FACES.

OH, I SEE.

NOTE FROM ALEX A.: Um… sorry 'bout this… Having thought it through, it doesn't really make sense to explain the Prophecy of 4 twice. I think everyone understood it the first time around. That's what happens when you have amnesia plot lines… So while we wait for Cassandra to finish her story, I bring you… **this special presentation!**

SO, "SNOW WHITE," YOU'RE ONE OF US, IS THAT RIGHT?

OH, YA, SURE!

YOU'RE DEFINITELY NOT AN IMPOSTER TRYING TO INFILTRATE OUR GROUP...

RIGHT?

UM... UM... NOT THAT I'M AWARE OF!

ANYHOW, WHY WOULD SOMEONE WANT TO INFILTRATE OUR GROUP? UNLESS, OF COURSE, IT WAS TO STEAL THE ONLY COPY OF THE PROPHECY OF 4.

THAT WOULD BE AN EXCELLENT REASON, ACTUALLY!

YES! BUT SINCE YOU'RE NOT AN IMPOSTER, THAT'S NOT WHY YOU'RE HERE, RIGHT? RIGHT?

UM... I'M NOT SURE I'M FOLLOWING THE...

EXCELLENT! SO TAKE THE BOOK. I CAN TRUST YOU COMPLETELY!

HERE!

UH... MASTER? WHAT DID YOU JUST DO?

YOU SEE, YOUNG SPECTRE, I USED SOMETHING CALLED REVERSE PSYCHOLOGY, AND...

AH! GO AFTER HIM!!!

MARTHAAAAA, WAKE UP...

I DIDN'T WANT TO RUN THE RISK OF YOU SABOTAGING MY PLANS AGAIN.

SO, WHAT DID YOU WANT TO TALK ABOUT?

I CAME TO...

ASK YOUR FORGIVENESS.

HMM?

I REJECTED YOU BACK THEN, I DIDN'T TRUST YOU. AND... YOU WENT DOWN THE WRONG PATH.

IT'S MY FAULT.

WHAT? HA HA HA! OF COURSE IT'S YOUR FAULT THAT I AM WHAT I AM. YOU STILL HAVE THE WEIGHT OF THE WORLD ON YOUR SHOULDERS, DON'T YOU?

THINKING YOU'RE THE WHOLE WORLD'S MOTHER? STOP IT, MARTHA. YOU'RE PATHETIC.

DO YOU REALLY THINK I WOULD HAVE TURNED OUT BETTER IF I HAD BEEN ABLE TO JOIN YOUR PRECIOUS SECRET ORGANIZATION?

COME ON, IT WOULD HAVE JUST BEEN ANOTHER OF YOUR PLANS TO KEEP AN EYE ON ME.

... I THINK IT WOULDN'T HAVE DONE YOU ANY HARM. I MEAN, LOOK AT WHAT YOU'VE BECOME.

WHAT I'VE BECOME? WHAT'S THE USE OF BECOMING ANYONE IN THIS WORLD? HUH?

THIS MAGNIFICENT WORLD YOU CLAIM TO PROTECT WILL SOON BE DESTROYED.

VIRTUALLY ALL LIFE WILL BE REDUCED TO ASHES.

AND MY SON WILL BE THE CHOSEN ONE OF THE DEMON THAT WILL LEAD THIS LAND OF FIRE!

GET THAT BOOK BACK!!!

WOW, I'M NOT BAD AT INFILTRATION MISSIONS AFTER ALL!

YOU WON'T GET PASSED ME!!

HA HA! HE'LL BE DEVOURED BY THE GREAT WOBASH!

THANKS A LOT! BUT THE PRINCESS IS IN ANOTHER CASTLE.

MM?

STOP! THERE IS NO DEMON! NO END OF THE WORLD! IT'S A LIE!

THAT'S NOT TRUE! THE STORIES ARE TRUE! HOW CAN YOU NOT SEE IT, MARTHA? THE SKY IS RED. THE EARTH KEEPS TREMBLING. THE VOLCANOES HAVE STARTED TO RUMBLE.

MAKHUS HAS APPEARED IN THE SKY. THE END IS UPON US!!

OF COURSE. AND YOU'RE THE MOTHER OF THE CHOSEN ONE WHO WILL REIGN OVER THE NEW LANDS OF FIRE. WHAT A GREAT ROLE...

STILL HAVE YOUR DIVINATORY POWERS TOO?

PFF. OF COURSE! TO PROVE IT... UM... YOU WON'T SNEEZE IN THE NEXT FIVE SECONDS!

ATCHOO!

YOU DID THAT ON PURPOSE!

NOT EVEN... THAT'S PRETTY FUNNY.

LISTEN, CASSANDRA. YOU HAVE ENORMOUS POTENTIAL, BUT YOU'RE STILL LIVING IN A WORLD OF MAKE-BELIEVE.

YOU'RE BEING TAKEN ADVANTAGE OF AGAIN, LIKE WITH...

BIG BEAVER.

I'LL ADMIT THAT BIG BEAVER MANIPULATED ME. BUT AT LEAST... HE MADE ME REALIZE WHAT THE WORLD IS REALLY LIKE.

CASSANDRA, I'M BEGGING YOU. STOP THIS INSANITY. THIS ISN'T THE END. I KNOW IT.

PREPARE TO LICK THE BOOK!

LICK! I THOUGHT WE WOULD HAVE TO PUT A DROP OF BLOOD ON IT, OR PERFORM A RITUAL SACRIFICE, I DON'T KNOW...

YA, WELL... MY PUBLISHER WAS A LITTLE SQUEAMISH ABOUT THE VIOLENCE...

I GUESS IT'S TRUE THAT CHILDREN COULD END UP READING THIS.

OH, STOP. YOU SHOULDN'T HIDE VIOLENCE FROM CHILDREN. YOU HAVE TO SHOW IT TO THEM AND EXPLAIN IT. THEY'LL HAVE TO DEAL WITH IT ONE DAY.

YOU MAKE A STRONG CASE, BUT YOU'RE FORGETTING ONE THING. IT'S THAT...

HELLO! CAN WE MOVE IT ALONG?

Place the tongue of the Chosen One here.

HONK

ARGHEU!

THE BOOK! FURY, GO GET IT!

JON! GO AFTER HIM!

UNDERSTOOD!

FOR EFFECT, PLAY RICHARD WAGNER'S "RIDE OF THE VALKYRIES" AS YOU READ THIS SCENE.

YOU MOCKED OUR PEOPLE, SO THIS THING IS OURS NOW!

WHATEVER IT IS..

TOC

NOT SO FAST!

THE BANANAS HAVE SOMETHING TO SAY ABOUT THAT.

ATTACK!!!

POF

CRAK

ADMIT IT, YOU'RE COMPLETELY DISORIENTED! YOU DON'T DARE TRUST YOUR OWN INSTINCTS.

YOU'RE WEAK.

YOU HAVE A BIG MOUTH.

KAKRA

WOW. THAT'S INTENSE.

THIS IS **TRULY** EPIC, DON'T YOU THINK?

ARGHEU!

IF YOU THINK ANYTHING YOU SAY OR DO WILL MAKE ME WALK AWAY, YOU'RE WRONG...

SISTER!

CAK

BRRR

BRROM

HANG ON!

HE HE HE! YOU SEE, I WAS RIGHT.

NOT ONLY WILL YOU NOT SAVE THE WORLD...

YOU WON'T EVEN SAVE... ME.

NO... NO!

IT CAN'T BE POSSIBLE!!!

HELLO, MARTHA.

THAT'S RIGHT. I'M NOT DEAD. AND AS LONG AS I'M ALIVE, BIG BEAVER, I'LL BE AROUND TO STOP YOU!

BUT... BUT...

I KILLED YOU!!

WING

ARGH!!! PAIN!!! RIGHT IN MY EYE!

BAM

MARTHA, IT'S REALLY ME.

I'M BACK.

THEODORE.

WHEN BUILDING Z EXPLODED, I WAS PROTECTED BY ONE OF AL'S SPECIAL SUITS AS I WAS BURIED UNDER TONS OF RUBBLE.

LUCKILY, BY DIGGING MY WAY THROUGH THE ROCKS, I FOUND A LITTLE CHAMBER WITH CLEAN WATER, AND I ATE THE INSECTS AND RATS THAT WERE PASSING THROUGH.

IT LOOKS LIKE YOU ATE A LOT OF THEM.

WELL, YES... I HAPPENED UPON RATS WITH A THING FOR MILKSHAKES.

ANYWAY, WITH ALL THE TRAINING I HAD AT THE AGENCY, I WAS ABLE TO SURVIVE FOR...

UM, HOW LONG WAS I IN THERE?

TWENTY YEARS.

THE END OF THE WORLD? HE HE. IT WASN'T THAT HARD.

THE EARTHQUAKES WERE CAUSED BY A MACHINE I INVENTED AND PLACED IN DIFFERENT UNDERGROUND LOCATIONS.

PLANET MAKHUS IS JUST A HOLOGRAM PROJECTED FROM THE MOON, JUST LIKE THE RED SKY.

AS FOR THE VOLCANOES, I JUST CHOSE THE PLACE WITH THE MOST VOLCANIC ACTIVITY. THE REDLANDS. IT WAS EASY!

AND THE BEES?

OH, THAT WASN'T ME. THE BEES REALLY ARE DISAPPEARING FROM THE PLANET. IT COULD BE A BIG PROBLEM!

SO YOU USED A PHONY PROPHECY TO CREATE A FALSE PANIC AND ORCHESTRATE YOUR RETURN FROM THE DEAD.

WHY?

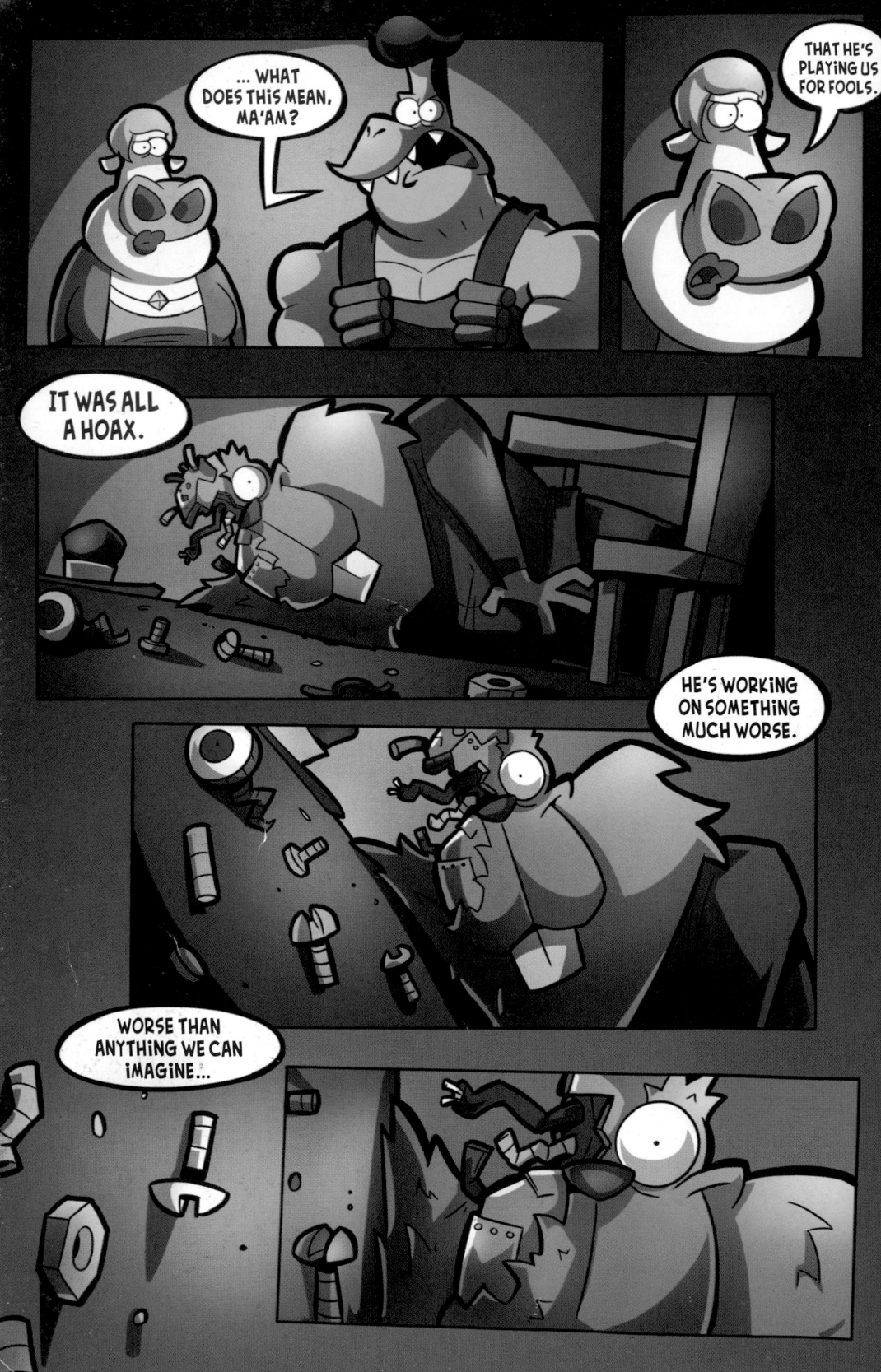

Alex A. is both author and illustrator of *Super Agent Jon Le Bon*. He discovered his love for drawing and creating cartoon characters at the early age of eight and has been at it ever since. His limitless imagination allows him to create new plots and twists and even completely new universes for his wacky and offbeat characters to evolve.

He'll tell you that his main source of inspiration is "all that exists but especially all that doesn't exist but lives in my imagination."

He's been successful as a freelance illustrator for books and magazines but his drive and determination has gotten him where he really wants to be – developing and drawing his own series.

The creation of Jon Le Bon is the culmination of many years of work, and gives us a series that is both very unique, intriguing and totally hilarious. Jon Le Bon, because of his innocence and fearlessness, can get himself in all sorts of trouble – but there's nothing he can't handle with a little help from his friends.

Alex A. lives in Montreal with his dog Wolfy and always shows up for book signings in his distinctive wool hat and colorful plaid pants, ready to entertain his young readers.

Follow Jon Le Bon in his
next big adventure:
TIME MACHINE

alexbd.com

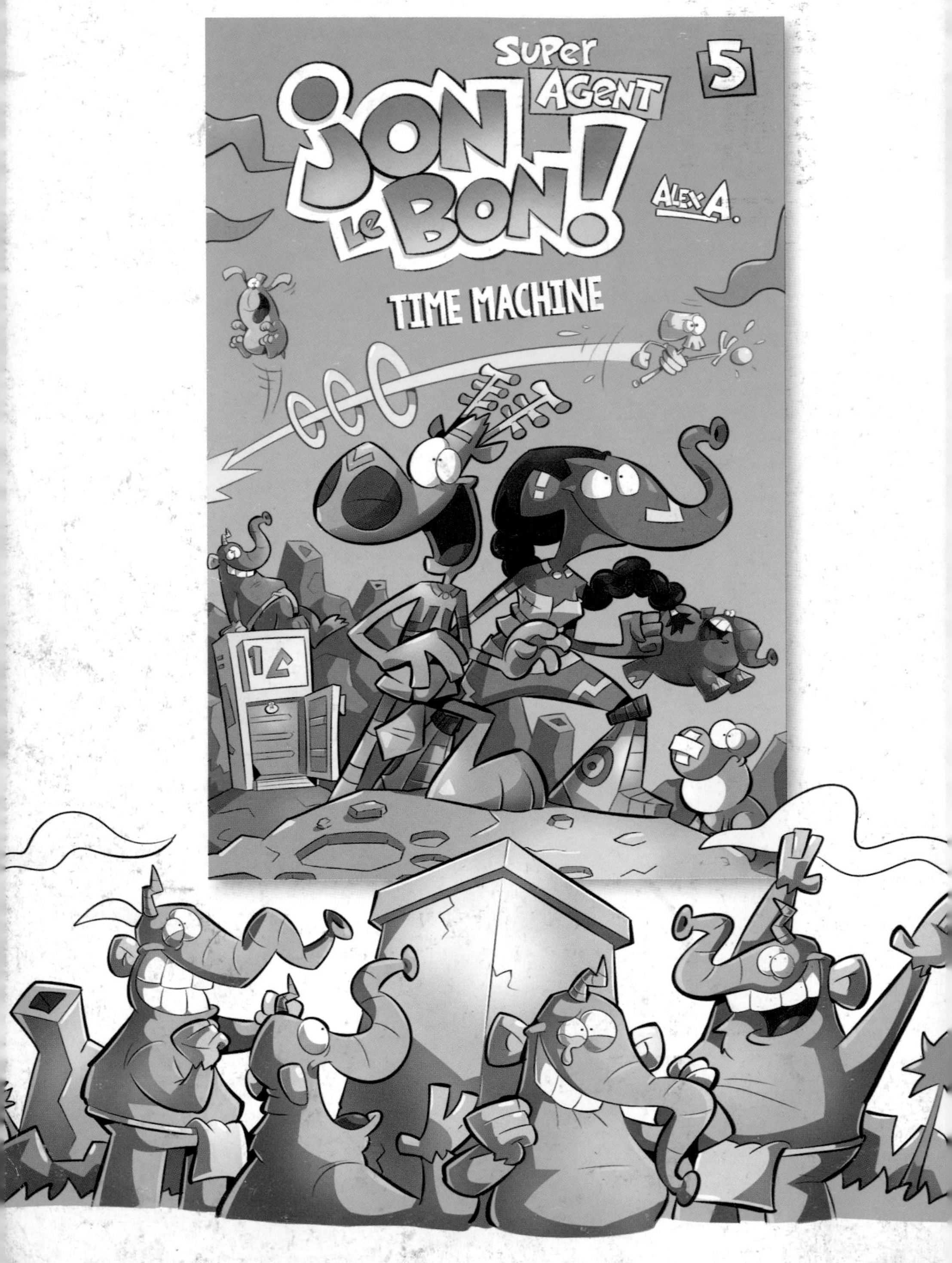
Super Agent
5
Jon Le Bon!
Alex A.
TIME MACHINE